Contents

A **pull-out answers section** (pages A1 to A8) appears in the centre of this book, between pages 20 and 21. It also gives simple guidance on how best to use this book. Remove this section before you begin working through the tests.

■ Underline the **two** words, one from each group, that are most **similar** in meaning

Example (<u>tired</u>, hungry, awake)   (<u>drowsy</u>, full, sad)

1. (jovial, serious, jostle)   (jolly, joke, jest)
2. (lazy, dazed, daft)   (greedy, idle, idol)
3. (permit, ticket, pocket)   (allow, travel, perform)
4. (there, adhere, affirm)   (branch, craft, stick)
5. (cartoon, character, animosity)   (animate, friendship, hatred)

■ In each of the following sentences, the word in capitals has three letters missing. Those three letters spell a word. Write the three-letter word on the line.

Example The baby **DK** her milk from the bottle.   <u>RAN</u>   (DRANK)

6. Peter tore his shirt on a thorny **BBLE** bush. _____
7. Molly was sitting behind a tall **PER** at the cinema. _____
8. The **SCE** of the river is high up in the mountains. _____
9. They **GIGG** uncontrollably at the puppet show. _____
10. She **BORED** her friend's dress for the party. _____

■ Find the missing number in each sequence. Write it on the line.

Example 20   22   24   26   28   <u>30</u>   (+ 2 each time)

11. 25   50   75   100   _____   150
12. 97   89   81   _____   65   57
13. 12   25   51   103   207   _____
14. 4   7   8   14   12   21   _____

■ Work out the answers. Write your answers on the lines.

15. Jameel set off with his pet dog, Grover, at **6.15** p.m. The walk to the park took them **16** minutes. They spent **18** minutes playing at the park but then Grover ran off. Jameel spent **10** minutes looking for Grover. When he found Grover it was time to go home, so they jogged home taking only **9** minutes to get there. What time did Jameel arrive back home? _____

16. Lucy went to visit her gran. She set off at **1.30** p.m. and caught the **1.46** p.m. bus. The bus arrived in Granville at **2.15** p.m. where Lucy had a **10**-minute wait for the next bus. She finally arrived at her gran's house **20** minutes later. How long was her journey altogether? _____

End of test

Score:		Time taken:		Target met?	

Target time: **10 minutes**

Find the missing number in each equation. Write it on the line.

Example 4 + 3 = 2 + ___5___

1. 70 ÷ 10 = 5 + _____
2. 14 ÷ 7 = 1 + _____
3. 110 ÷ 10 = 19 – _____
4. 87 – 84 = 96 – _____
5. 81 ÷ 9 = 36 ÷ _____

Underline the **two** words, one from each group, that are most **opposite** in meaning.

Example (old, son, home) (new, grandfather, house)

6. (defend, deny, claim) (depart, attack, test)
7. (mumble, grumble, humble) (complain, proud, mutter)
8. (contract, expect, agree) (contain, expand, explode)
9. (sneeze, pray, curse) (spell, bless, cast)
10. (secret, private, neighbour) (hidden, reconcile, public)

Match the number codes to the words. Use these to help you work out the answers to the questions. Write your answers on the lines.

WORD   AFTER   DOOR   DRAFT   9113   7139   93862   86253

What is the code for:

11. **RAFT**? _____
12. **ROAD**? _____
13. **TREAT**? _____
14. What does the code **13953** mean? _____

Circle the letter next to the **true** statement for each question.

15. Table mats help to keep the heat off a table. Cork is a material which absorbs a lot of heat.

If the above statements are true, which one of the following statements must also be true?
A. Table mats keep the table tidy.
B. Hot drinks can be spilled easily.
C. People put their plates on table mats.
D. Cork is a good material for table mats.

16. Mrs White must catch the **8.30** a.m. train to arrive at work on time. Mrs White caught the **8.45** a.m. train to work on Monday.

If the above statements are true, which one of the following statements must also be true?
A. Mrs White overslept on Monday.
B. Mrs White was late for work on Monday.
C. Mrs White left home 10 minutes late.
D. Mrs White likes trains.

End of test.

Score:		Time taken:		Target met?	

■ Underline the **two** words, one from each group, that will complete the sentence in the best way.

> **Example Mother** is to (lady, home, <u>daughter</u>) as **father** is to (<u>son</u>, old, beard).

1. **Jump** is to (dance, walk, leap) as **run** is to (quick, sprint, hop).
2. **Doe** is to (deer, buck, calf) as **nanny** is to (horse, billy, granny).
3. **Judge** is to (honour, courtroom, law) as **surgeon** is to (stadium, theatre, hospital).
4. **Lorry** is to (oil, diesel, power) as **torch** is to (switch, light, battery).
5. **Mimic** is to (cope, imitate, play) as **believable** is to (reward, credible, gratified).

■ Use the information given to answer each sum. Write your answer as a **letter.**

> **Example** A = 4   B = 2   C = 3   D = 6   E = 10   **A + D =** <u> E </u>   (4 + 6 = 10)

6. A = 42   B = 7   C = 6   D = 43   E = 41   **B × C =** _____
7. A = 15   B = 17   C = 21   D = 8   E = 9   **2(C – B) =** _____
8. A = 25   B = 45   C = 35   D = 38   E = 18   **E + B – D =** _____
9. A = 16   B = 49   C = 4   D = 39   E = 15   **C × A – E =** _____
10. A = 0   B = 19   C = 71   D = 89   E = 18   **3A + D – C =** _____

■ Find the missing letter pair in the sequence. Write it on the line. Use the alphabet to help you.

A B C D E F G H I J K L M N O P Q R S T U V W X Y Z

> **Example** RS   UV   XY   AB   <u> DE </u>   (+3, +3)

11. AZ BY CX DW _____
12. VY UZ TA SB _____
13. MV NW _____ SY WZ
14. VZ YW XX AU ZV CS _____

■ Work out the answers. Write your answers on the lines.

15. There are **3** people in the waiting room at a doctor's surgery. Susie's appointment is at **10.15** a.m. and Callum's appointment is half an hour later. Mick's appointment is halfway between Susie's appointment and Callum's. If the doctor is running **10** minutes late to see each patient, what time will he see Mick? _____

16. Yelena sends **10** text messages per day to her friends. If each message costs 8p to send, how much will it cost her to send text messages every day for one week? _____

End of test.

Score: [   ]   Time taken: [   ]   Target met? [   ]

Target time: 10 minutes

Underline the pair of words that are most **opposite** in meaning.

Example (<u>under</u>, <u>over</u>)   (aloof, aloft)   (irritate, anger)

1. (revile, reveal)   (conceal, show)   (reconcile, congeal)

2. (temporary, permanent)   (rhythm, template)   (permeate, pierce)

3. (quieten, decrepit)   (descent, ascent)   (decline, decent)

4. (brazen, burnt)   (beg, plead)   (condemn, praise)

5. (divide, dispense)   (graze, trim)   (assemble, disband)

Find **one** missing letter that completes **both** pairs of words. Write it on the lines.

Example truc [_k_] ite   lic [_k_] now

6. roa [__] ed   floo [__] eal

7. sigh [__] wist   star [__] rap

8. stee [__] ost   schoo [__] amb

9. stee [__] ass   ski [__] rey

10. clas [__] word   mis [__] wim

Using the alphabet to help you, find the letter pair that completes each sentence. Write it on the line.

A B C D E F G H I J K L M N O P Q R S T U V W X Y Z

Example XY is to **TU** as **NO** is to ___JK___.   (–4, –4)

1. **MW** is to **QC** as **SU** is to _____.

2. **GK** is to **BH** as **CN** is to _____.

13. **LI** is to **RG** as **VD** is to _____.

14. **JC** is to **QX** as **GM** is to _____.

Work out the answers. Write your answers on the lines.

5. Ethel baked a dozen cup cakes for the village fete. Half the cakes had pink icing and half had blue icing. **2** of the cakes with blue icing and **3** of the cakes with pink icing had a cherry on top. The rest of the pink cakes and 1 of the blue cakes had chocolate sprinkles on. The cakes without cherries on top were in white cases and the rest were in green cases. How many cakes were in white cases?

_____

6. Yumiko collects animal stickers. She has **30** cat stickers, **15** horse stickers, **19** dog stickers and **11** rabbit stickers. One-third of the horse stickers are round and the rest are square. One-fifth of the cat stickers are square and the rest are round. All the dog stickers are square. All the rabbit stickers are round. What proportion of **all** the stickers are round? _____

End of test.

Score:		Time taken:		Target met?	

Find the **four-letter word** hidden across two or more consecutive words in each sentence below. The order of the letters must stay the same. Underline the word and write it on the line.

Example How many cakes have you ea<u>ten </u>today?   <u>   tent   </u>

1. I wish opportunities like that were more common!   _____

2. Please place the gazebo at the back of the garden.   _____

3. The director made episodes for a daily show.   _____

4. The drop in temperature was unwelcome.   _____

5. The little boy was accidentally shut in the cupboard.   _____

■ Underline the **two** words in each row that contain all the **same** letters.

Example two   <u>now</u>   was   <u>won</u>   you

6. pales   peals   pears   pared   plain

7. cases   cares   races   stare   raced

8. times   tiles   tries   items   miles

9. coast   crust   stoat   coats   stunt

10. stars   stare   stain   store   rates

■ Work out the missing number and write it on the line.

Example 3 [5] 2   4 [6] 2   5 [<u> 8 </u>] 3
(a + b = ?, where a represents the number on the left and b represents the number on the right)

11. 8 [64] 8   6 [36] 6   5 [_____] 5

12. 17 [34] 2   26 [104] 4   52 [_____] 4

13. 40 [10] 4   25 [5] 5   100 [_____] 4

14. 64 [32] 2   108 [54] 2   360 [_____] 2

■ Work out the answers. Write your answers on the lines.

15. How many more days are there altogether in March, April and May than in June and July?
_____

16. If the day after tomorrow is Friday, what was the day before yesterday? _____

End of test

Score:		Time taken:		Target met?	

Target time: 10 minutes

In each of the sentences below, the word in capitals has three letters missing.
Those three letters spell a word. Write the three-letter word on the line.

Example The baby **DK** her milk from the bottle. ___RAN___ (DRANK)

1. He found old **CHES** to wear in the attic. _____

2. He **SCBED** the floor to make it clean. _____

3. The **ST** dog had no home. _____

4. The horse **TTED** round the field. _____

5. He **K** many of the answers to the quiz. _____

Underline the **two** words, one from each group, that together make one new
word. The word from the first group comes first.

Example (<u>drain</u>, gutter, ditch)   (rain, <u>pipe</u>, flow)   (drainpipe)

6. (over, under, around)   (hope, haul, carry)

7. (face, head, foot)   (ache, pain, illness)

8. (met, new, people)   (hidden, hod, find)

9. (prim, victory, old)   (ate, eaten, lion)

10. (pop, music, dance)   (market, food, pies)

Find the missing number in each equation. Write it on the line.

Example 4 + 3 = 2 + ___5___

11. $90 \div 9 = 2 \times$ _____   13. $49 - 17 = 4 \times$ _____

12. $21 \times 3 = 100 -$ _____   14. $99 \div 11 = 18 \div$ _____

Work out the answers. Write your answers on the lines.

15. 12 cars are parked on Marcel's street. Some of the cars are sports cars, some are saloons and **3** are hatchbacks. There are **3** red cars, **4** blue cars, **2** silver cars and the rest are black. All the hatchbacks and **1** of the saloons are blue. The sports cars are either red or black. If both the silver cars and **2** of the red cars are saloons, how many sports cars are there altogether? _____

16. Mrs Cleaver is posting **5** parcels. Parcel 1 is heavier than parcel 3 but lighter than parcels 4 and 2. Parcel 3 is heavier than parcel 5. If parcel 2 is the heaviest parcel, which is the lightest?

_____   End of test.

Score:		Time taken:		Target met?	

⬇
■ If these words were listed in alphabetical order, which word would come **last**?
Write the answer on the line.

Example drink   drain   dire   driver   drawn   ____driver____

1. enlist   endanger   enrage   endeavour   enough   _____
2. higher   hirer   highest   height   horrific   _____
3. strawberry   stripey   stricken   strength   strengthen   _____
4. malicious   malevolent   malformed   militant   malfunction   _____
5. distress   destroy   distant   dissatisfied   desperate   _____

■ In each group, three words go together and two are the odd ones out. Underline the **two** words that do **not** go with the other three.

Example comprehend   understand   <u>confuse</u>   <u>unsure</u>   grasp

6. toad   frog   newt   chameleon   lizard
7. saucepan   colander   sieve   xylophone   piano
8. guest   restaurant   book   hotel   pub
9. motorway   bypass   path   road   bridleway
10. square   triangle   trapezium   circle   parallelogram

■ The word in square brackets has been made by some of the letters from the two outside words. Make a new word in the middle of the second group of words in the same way. Write the new word on the line.

Example (hire [hurt] truck)   (liar [___leap___] preys)

11. (pile [play] years)   (main [_____] dents)   13. (vest [tear] harm)   (lift [_____] clef)
12. (thin [hand] acids)   (show [_____] opals)   14. (moat [omen] need)   (cake [_____] stop)

■ Use the word's definition to help you fill in the missing letters.

Example G <u>E</u> N E <u>R</u> <u>O</u> US   giving, charitable   (GENEROUS)

15. P __ E __ __ T __ R   marauder, killer, hunter
16. CR __ __ TI __ __   imaginative, resourceful, artistic

End of test

Underline the **two** words, one from each group, that are most **similar** in meaning.

Example (tired, hungry, awake)   (drowsy, full, sad)

1. (coast, approve, bombard)   (explode, pelt, cliff)
2. (robe, shopper, habit)   (custom, hood, pamphlet)
3. (prominent, memory, recall)   (external, forgotten, outstanding)
4. (sore, calm, brisk)   (harsh, soothe, bask)
5. (lament, straight, upset)   (distress, double, twist)

Change the first word into the last word. Only change **one** letter at a time, making two new four-letter words in the middle. Write the new words.

Example TRAP [_TRAM_][_PRAM_] PROM

6. GAME [_____][_____] TILE   9. FILM [_____][_____] PALE
7. LICE [_____][_____] MALE   10. WOOD [_____][_____] GOAT
8. WINE [_____][_____] SANG

Using the alphabet to help you, crack the code. Write your answer on the line.
A B C D E F G H I J K L M N O P Q R S T U V W X Y Z

Example If the code for **TOP** is **UPQ**, what is the code for **TIP**?   _UJQ_
(+1 from word to code)

11. If the code for **TABLE** is **GZYOV**, what is the code for **SCREEN**? _____
12. If the code for **JUMPER** is **KVNQFS**, what does the code **TDBSG** mean? _____
13. If the code for **COMPUTER** is **XLNKFGVI**, what is the code for **ELEVATOR**? _____
14. If the code for **DENIM** is **FGPKO**, what is the code for **FABRIC**? _____

Work out the answers. Write your answers on the lines.

15. Trevor's watch is 11 minutes fast. If his watch says the time is **8.45** a.m., what is the real time?
_____

16. The **5.05** p.m. bus from Reading to Wargrave takes 1 hour 15 minutes to reach its destination. If the bus is running 17 minutes late, what time will it arrive in Wargrave? _____

End of test.

Score:		Time taken:		Target met?	

⬇
■ From the five possible answers on the right, underline the word which goes equally well with both pairs of words in brackets.

Example (otter, walrus) (stopper, stamp) dolphin safe <u>seal</u> post close

1. (money, vault)   (protected, harmless)   pound   cash   safe   careful   bank
2. (coach, teach)   (rail, track)   learn   engine   drive   train   lecture
3. (breeze, cool)   (admirer, supporter)   fan   wind   follower   blow   idol
4. (orchestra, group)   (ring, loop)   choir   pop   circle   band   gang
5. (satisfactory, good)   (penalty, fee)   fine   pay   adequate   cost   goal

■ Find the missing number in each equation. Write it on the line.

Example $4 + 3 = 2 +$ ___5___

6. $37 × 2 + 1 = 100 - 21 -$ _____
7. $(27 + 3) × 3 = 31 +$ _____
8. $125 ÷ 5 × 3 = 30 +$ _____

9. $4(18 ÷ 3) = 23 +$ _____
10. $360 ÷ 6 = 140 + 20 -$ _____

■ Find the missing letter pair in the sequence. Write it on the line. Use the alphabet to help you.

A B C D E F G H I J K L M N O P Q R S T U V W X Y Z

Example RS   UV   XY   AB   __DE__   (+3, +3)

11. AZ _____ CX DW EV
12. _____ NO PQ RS TU

13. QW AS PU BT OS CU _____
14. AM _____ AO DP AQ

■ Circle the letter next to the **true** statement.

15. Kitchen utensils are used for preparing food. A wooden spoon is used for preparing food.

    If the above statements are true, which one of the following statements must also be true?
    A. All utensils are kept in the kitchen.
    B. A ladle is another kitchen utensil.
    C. Wooden spoons are kitchen utensils.
    D. All spoons are made of wood.

■ Work out the answer. Write your answer on the line.

16. Maya thinks of a number. She doubles it, subtracts 12 then divides it by 4. She gets the answer 12. What number did she think of? _____

End of test

Score: _____   Time taken: _____   Target met? _____

Target time: 10 minutes

In each group, three words go together and two are the odd ones out. Underline the **two** words that do **not** go with the other three.

Example comprehend   understand   <u>confuse</u>   <u>unsure</u>   grasp

1. arrive   dodge   avoid   devoid   evade
2. beige   tangerine   tan   fawn   orange
3. gem   diamond   platinum   gold   silver
4. defect   failing   industry   deficiency   sufficient
5. chisel   axel   screwdriver   podium   spanner

In each of the sentences below, the word in capitals has three letters missing. Those three letters spell a word. Write the three-letter word on the line.

Example The baby **DK** her milk from the bottle.   RAN   (DRANK)

6. She had **FORTEN** the code for the lock. _____
7. He didn't like vegetables, especially **ROTS**. _____
8. They **WID** they didn't have to go to school. _____
9. She **NED** him that the test would be difficult. _____
0. The river **FED** rapidly downhill. _____

Using the alphabet to help you, crack the code. Write your answer on the line.

A B C D E F G H I J K L M N O P Q R S T U V W X Y Z

Example If the code for **TOP** is **UPQ**, what is the code for **TIP**?   UJQ

(+1 from word to code)

1. If **JACKET** is written in code as **GXZHBQ**, what is the code for **COAT**? _____
2. If the code for **CHAPTER** is **XSZKGVI**, what is the code for **BOOKMARK**? _____
3. If the code **BTQKR** means **CURLS**, what does the code **GZHQ** mean? _____
4. If the code for **LIPSTICK** is **PMTWXMGO**, what is the code for **MAKEUP**? _____

Work out the answers. Write your answers on the lines.

5. Holly goes back to school 4 days later than Li who goes back 3 days before Ava. If Ava starts back at school on 9 September, what date does Holly start back? _____

6. Celia is 5 years older than Sandra's sister who is half Sandra's age. Sandra is 16, how old is Celia?

_____

End of test.

Score:	Time taken:	Target met?

Move one letter from the first word to the second word to make two new words. Write the two new words on the lines.

Example liver, down ___live___ , ___drown___ (move the r)

1. linked, give _____ , _____
2. create, sham _____ , _____
3. crack, rumble _____ , _____
4. swing, serves _____ , _____
5. window, ever _____ , _____

Use the information given to answer each sum. Write your answer as a **letter**.

Example A = 4   B = 2   C = 3   D = 6   E = 10   **A + D =** ___E___   (4 + 6 = 10)

6. A = 5   B = 24   C = 8   D = 16   E = 15   **(B ÷ C) × A =** _____
7. A = 1.5   B = 3   C = 4.5   D = 6   E = 7   **(A × B) + A =** _____
8. A = 8   B = –1   C = 7   D = 9   E = –9   **A – B =** _____
9. A = 12   B = 11   C = 3   D = 14   E = 31   **(D × C) – E =** _____
10. A = 30   B = 25   C = 12   D = 24   E = 18   **5(E – C) =** _____

From the five possible answers on the right, underline the word which goes equally well with both pairs of words in brackets.

Example (otter, walrus)   (stopper, stamp)   dolphin   safe   <u>seal</u>   post   close

11. (main, prime)   (iron, gold)   lead   metal   rock   silver   central
12. (din, racket)   (argue, disagree)   fight   noise   row   annoy   rumpus
13. (bread, baguette)   (lounge, idle)   relax   toast   roll   loaf   laze
14. (iris, eye)   (student, school)   eyeball   pupil   eyelash   teacher   learn

---

Work out the answers. Write your answers on the lines.

15. A bar of chocolate is shared between **3** children. The bar of chocolate is made up of **16** squares. Sammy eats half of the chocolate. If Jen and Franco share the rest of the chocolate equally between them, how many squares do they each get? _____

16. Ella has **45** gerbils. One-third of the gerbils are white. **12** are brown. The rest are grey. How many grey gerbils does Ella have? _____

End of test

Score:		Time taken:		Target met?	

Target time: 10 minutes

■ Underline the word in brackets that is most **opposite** in meaning to the word in capitals.

Example BEAUTIFUL   (fair, <u>ugly</u>, pretty, graceful)

1. WASTE   (wise, wrest, construe, conserve, contort)
2. COMPLEX   (complete, straightforward, complicated, keen)
3. HOLLOW   (opaque, solid, empty, shallow)
4. ROBUST   (dishevelled, dedicate, delicate, rebound)
5. DISALLOW   (forgo, let, leave, forebode)

■ Find **one** missing letter that completes **both** pairs of words. Write it on the lines.

Example truc [_k_] ite   lic [_k_] now

6. cinem [__] isle   arom [__] ble
7. car [__] ickle   blanke [__] error
8. chim [__] lbow   sleev [__] njoy

9. craz [__] ield   sla [__] awn
10. see [__] irt   bon [__] aze

■ The word in square brackets has been made by some of the letters from the two outside words. Make a new word in the middle of the second group of words in the same way. Write the new word on the line.

Example (hire [hurt] truck)   (liar [_____leap_____] preys)

1. (sting [nasty] clay)   (bling [_____] shoe)
2. (moody [dryer] retro)   (drips [_____] atlas)
3. (drink [knit] tanks)   (stray [_____] eight)
4. (ovens [evict] pictures)   (blood [_____] liveries)

■ Work out the answers. Write your answers on the lines.

5. Clarence's family is eating dinner. Clarence finishes his meal before his sister Mary finishes hers. His brothers Bill and Tod both finish their food before Clarence. Clarence's father finishes his meal after Clarence but before his daughter. Who is next to last to finish eating? _____

6. Six children are taking part in an Easter egg hunt. Shiv collects more eggs than Jana but fewer eggs than Sarah. Kim collects the fewest eggs. Danny collects more eggs than Bren, who collects more than Sarah. Who collects the second fewest number of eggs? _____

End of test.

Score:		Time taken:		Target met?	

⬇
■ Find the missing number in each sequence. Write it on the line.

Example 20   22   24   26   28   <u>30</u>   (+2 each time)

1. 97   85   _____   61   49   37
2. 16   8   _____   −8   −16   −24
3. 3   16   42   94   198   _____

4. 1680   240   _____   8   2
5. 12   36   108   324   _____

....

■ Underline the **two** words, one from each group, that together make one new word. The word from the first group comes first.

Example (<u>drain</u>, gutter, ditch)   (rain, <u>pipe</u>, flow)   (drainpipe)

6. (screw, twist, bolt)   (van, driver, lorry)
7. (duvet, pillow, bed)   (case, file, holdall)
8. (in, around, behind)   (fold, crease, iron)
9. (picture, art, gold)   (frame, sell, work)
10. (rubber, bounce, spring)   (dive, board, height)

....

■ Match the number codes to the words. One code is missing. Use these to help you work out the answers to the questions. Write your answers on the lines.

PILE   LEAP   PACE   SALE   9165   2185   2765

What is the code for:
11. **SLEEP**? _____   12. **PLACE**? _____   13. **LEASE**? _____
14. What does the code **61295** mean? _____

....

■ Circle the letter next to the **true** statement.

15. Carnivores eat meat while vegetarians do not eat meat. Tigers eat meat.

    If the above statements are true, which one of the following statements must also be true?
    A. Tigers cannot eat vegetables.   C. Tigers are carnivores.
    B. Tigers hunt animals to eat.   D. Baby tigers eat little animals.

....

■ Work out the answer. Write your answer on the line.

16. If the first Sunday in May is **5 May**, how many Saturdays are there in June? _____

End of test

Score:	Time taken:	Target met?

Target time: 10 minutes

Underline the word in brackets that is **closest** in meaning to the word in capitals.

Example LUCKY   (unlucky, <u>fortunate</u>, kind, helpful)

1. PERSUADE   (peruse, coax, utilise, stitch)
2. ESCAPE   (prison, elude, rude, assess)
3. GLOWER   (surprise, shine, scowl, bore)
4. MERGE   (magnify, ruse, microscope, fuse)
5. GRAZE   (hay, scrape, barn, grease)

Underline the **two** words, one from each group, that will complete the sentence in the best way.

Example Mother is to (lady, home, <u>daughter</u>) as **father** is to (<u>son</u>, old, beard).

6. **Quadrant** is to (grid, matrix, four) as **tripod** is to (camera, three, tricycle).
7. **Erupt** is to (storm, volcano, explode) as **fallacy** is to (truth, myth, phantom).
8. **Hanger** is to (shirt, aeroplane, wardrobe) as **hook** is to (curved, coat, grip).
9. **Swan** is to (lake, cygnet, duck) as **eagle** is to (fly, beak, eaglet).
10. **Melon** is to (fruit, pips, lemon) as **plum** is to (skin, lump, juicy).

Find the missing letters or symbols in the sequence. Write them on the line. Use the alphabet to help you.

A B C D E F G H I J K L M N O P Q R S T U V W X Y Z

Example RS   UV   XY   AB   <u>DE</u>   (+3, +3)

11. WT   HO   YU   IP   AV   JQ   _____
12. HD   FB   _____   BX   ZV   XT
13. *!£   !£*   £*!   *!£   _____   £*!
14. LcM   NdN   PeO   RfP   TgQ   _____

Work out the answers. Write your answers on the lines.

15. How many days after New Year's Eve is 12 March in a leap year? _____

16. If the day before yesterday was Monday, what will the day two days after tomorrow be?
_____

End of test.

Score:		Time taken:		Target met?	

1–5. Look at the words in groups A, B and C. For each of the words below, choose the correct group and write its letter on the line.

A	B	C
lamb	ewe	buck

kid _____   bull _____   nanny _____   foal _____   sow _____

stag _____   billy _____   peahen _____   gosling _____   doe _____

Use the information given to answer each sum. Write your answer as a **letter**.

Example A = 4   B = 2   C = 3   D = 6   E = 10   **A + D =** __E__   (4 + 6 = 10)

6. A = 13   B = 12   C = 100   D = 65   E = 56   **B × A – E =** _____

7. A = 40   B = 30   C = 60   D = 70   E = 80   **(D – A) + B =** _____

8. A = 5.5   B = 7.5   C = 2.5   D = 0.5   E = 4   **B + D – C =** _____

9. A = 12   B = 18   C = 16   D = 20   E = 24   **E ÷ A + B =** _____

10. A = 125   B = 45   C = 57   D = 26   E = 23   **(A – C) – B =** _____

Using the alphabet to help you, find the letter pair that completes each sentence. Write it on the line.

A B C D E F G H I J K L M N O P Q R S T U V W X Y Z

Example **XY** is to **TU** as **NO** is to __JK__.   (–4, –4)

11. **QD** is to **XG** as **SS** is to _____.

13. **PD** is to **KW** as **FY** is to _____.

12. **YA** is to **DS** as **KF** is to _____.

14. **NV** is to **JY** as **ER** is to _____.

Work out the answers. Write your answers on the lines.

15. Harshida went to the sweet shop to buy some sweets. She bought **8** chocolate mice, **5** liquorice, **6** fruities, **4** toffees, **8** eclairs and **10** mints. The mints, eclairs and fruities were in striped wrappers, the toffees were in plain silver wrappers and the chocolate mice and liquorice were unwrapped. Half the striped wrappers were silver and gold and the rest were green and blue. How many sweets had silver on their wrappers? _____

16. Jeremy has 16 pet hamsters. One-quarter of the hamsters are white, one-quarter are brown, 3 hamsters are ginger and the rest are golden. Half of the white hamsters, 3 of the golden hamsters and 2 of the brown hamsters have black patches on their fur. 2 of the ginger hamsters and 3 of the brown hamsters have white paws. How many of the hamsters have some black fur? _____

End of test

Score:		Time taken:		Target met?	

Target time: **10 minutes**

In each group, three words go together and two are the odd ones out. Underline the **two** words that do **not** go with the other three.

Example comprehend   understand   <u>confuse</u>   <u>unsure</u>   grasp

1. comply   obey   disagree   consent   reject
2. weigh   ruler   measure   estimate   scales
3. recall   recollect   distinguish   remember   redistribute
4. retina   iris   classroom   pupil   blink
5. speed   dawdle   lag   accelerate   loiter

Underline the pair of words that are most **similar** in meaning.

Example (rain, snow)   (sea, sand)   <u>(earth, mud)</u>

6. (career, mountain)   (clamber, climb)   (struggle, slippery)
7. (precise, exact)   (prelude, finale)   (dramatic, actor)
8. (envious, jealous)   (tender, tendril)   (envisage, enliven)
9. (rein, reign)   (measure, matter)   (rule, regulation)
10. (feather, fleece)   (flicker, glimmer)   (shadow, dark)

Underline **one** word in each set of brackets to complete the sentence best.

Example The bus (wheels, <u>conductor</u>, passenger) collected the (food, <u>fares</u>, ride) from the (<u>passengers</u>, babies, driver).

11. The (jockey, driver, pilot) rode his (car, robot, horse) swiftly around the (course, runway, motorway).
12. The (teacher, surgeon, clerk) asked the (patients, students, prisoners) to turn over their exam papers and start the (test, clock, race).
13. (Potatoes, bananas, beans) grow on (vines, trees, rocks) in hot (gardens, rivers, countries) such as St Lucia.
14. The judge asked the (congregation, audience, jury) if they had reached a (verdict, victim, criminal) at the end of the (programme, performance, trial).

Use the word's definition to help you fill in the missing letters.

Example G <u>E</u> N E R <u>O</u> US   giving, charitable   (GENEROUS)

15. E L __ B __ __ A __ __   intricate, detailed, convoluted
16. E __ O L __ T __ __ N   progress, development, advancement

End of test.

Score:		Time taken:		Target met?	

■ Work out the missing number and write it on the line.

Example 3 [5] 2   4 [6] 2   5 [_8_] 3
(a + b = ?, where a represents the number on the left and b represents the number on the right)

1. 51 [86] 35   13 [18] 5   135 [_____] 20
2. 49 [134] 80   35 [50] 10   40 [_____] 23
3. 66 [52] 24   23 [28] 5   6 [_____] 6
4. 26 [10] 6   32 [14] 4   14 [_____] 4
5. 100 [20] 20   400 [90] 40   200 [_____] 40

■ Rearrange the word in capitals to make another word that goes with the first two. Write it on the line.

Example arm   finger   GEL   _LEG_

6. moustache   hair   BARED   _____
7. god   saint   ANGLE   _____
8. cry   wail   TASER   _____
9. butcher   tailor   BREAK   _____
10. jumped   bounced   PETAL   _____

■ The words in the sentences below have been muddled up and an extra, unnecessary word has been added to each. Unjumble the sentences, then remove the extra word so that the sentences make sense. Cross out the extra word.

Example your how children many are ~~you~~ there in class?
(How many children are there in your class?)

11. wild in wolves are hunt that packs in animals
12. I school went London week on a to Zoo trip last yesterday
13. the swooped eagle its suddenly down below perch from
14. different many there of bird is types are

■ Work out the answers. Write your answers on the lines.

15. Seven horses are taking part in a race. Zoomer is in last place. Carrot is three places ahead of Zoomer. Biscuit is two places ahead of Carrot. Pixie is in first place and Thunderbolt is two places behind her. Dash is three places behind Biscuit. In what place must Rosie be? _____

16. Dina's cake recipe has five steps. The recipe says whisk the eggs before weighing the flour. It says mix the sugar and butter together after measuring out the milk but before whisking the eggs. The recipe says turn on the oven after the first two steps are completed. What is the fourth step of the recipe?

_____

End of test

| Score: | Time taken: | Target met? |

Notes for parents, tutors, teachers and other adult helpers

- **Verbal Reasoning 5** is designed for 10- and 11-year-olds, but may also be suitable for some older children.

- Remove this pull-out section before giving the book to the child.

- Before the child begins work on the first test, read together the instructions on page 2, headed **Introduction**. As you do so, look together at **Section 1 Test 1** and point out to the child the different elements.

- As each question type is introduced for the first time within a particular test, an example is given. Where question types recur throughout the book, the same example is provided. This is deliberate: the example will act as a useful reminder, but children will not need to work through it repeatedly from scratch.

- Make sure that the child understands how to answer the questions and that he or she has a pencil and eraser. You should also ensure that the child is able to see a clock or a watch.

- Explain to the child how he or she should go about timing the test. Alternatively, you may wish to time the test yourself. When the child has finished the test, one of you should complete the **Time taken** box, which appears at the end of the test.

- Mark the child's work using this pull-out section, giving one mark for each correct answer (unless advised otherwise). Then complete the **Score** box at the end of the test.

- The table below shows you how to mark the **Target met?** box and the **Action** notes give you some guidance as you plan the next step. However, these are suggestions only. Please use your own judgement as you decide how best to proceed.

Score	Time taken	Target met?	Action
1–8	Any	Not yet	Give the child the previous book in the series. Provide help and support as needed.
9–13	Any	Not yet	Encourage the child to keep practising using the tests in this book. The child may need to repeat some tests. If so, wait a few weeks, or the child may simply remember the correct answers. Provide help and support as needed.
14–16	Over target – child took too long	Not yet	
14–16	On target – child took suggested time or less	Yes	Encourage the child to keep practising using further tests in this book, and to move on to the next book when you think this is appropriate.

- Whatever the test score, always encourage the child to have another go at the questions that he or she got wrong without looking at the solutions. If the child's answers are still incorrect, work through these questions together. Demonstrate the correct method if necessary.

- If the child struggles with particular question types, help him or her to develop the strategies needed.

The **Understanding Reasoning** series, also available from Schofield & Sims, provides clear explanations on how to answer reasoning questions. It also provides 'Tips for tests' and 'Tips for revision'. For further details on this vnd other series that help children and young people to prepare for school selection tests, and for free downloads relating to the **Rapid Reasoning Tests**, visit www.schofieldandsims.co.uk

Answers

Section 1 Test 1 (page 4)

1. jovial, jolly
2. lazy, idle
3. permit, allow
4. adhere, stick
5. animosity, hatred
6. RAM (BRAMBLE)
7. SON (PERSON)
8. OUR (SOURCE)
9. LED (GIGGLED)
10. ROW (BORROWED)
11. 125 (+25)
12. 73 (−8)
13. 415 (double it and add 1)
14. 16 (leapfrogging +4, +7)
15. 7.08 p.m./eight minutes past seven/19:08
16. 1 hour and 15 minutes

Section 1 Test 2 (page 5)

1. 2
2. 1
3. 8
4. 93
5. 4
6. defend, attack
7. humble, proud
8. contract, expand
9. curse, bless
10. private, public
11. 3862
12. 3189
13. 23582
14. ORDER
15. D
16. B

Section 1 Test 3 (page 6)

1. leap, sprint (Leap is a synonym for jump; sprint is a synonym for run.)
2. buck, billy (Doe is a female rabbit and buck is a male rabbit; nanny is a female goat and billy is a male goat.)
3. courtroom, theatre (A judge works in a courtroom inside a courthouse and a surgeon works in a theatre inside a hospital.)
4. diesel, battery (A lorry is powered by diesel and a torch by a battery.)
5. imitate, credible (Imitate is a synonym for mimic; credible is a synonym for believable.)
6. A ($7 \times 6 = 42$)
7. D ($[21 − 17] \times 2 = 8$)
8. A ($18 + 45 − 38 = 25$)
9. B ($4 \times 16 − 15 = 49$)
10. E ($3 \times 0 + 89 − 71 = 18$)
11. EV (+1, −1)
12. RC (−1, +1)
13. PX (first letter +1, +2, +3, +4; second letter +1)
14. BT (first letter +3, −1; second letter −3, +1)
15. 10.40 a.m./twenty to eleven/10:40
16. £5.60 ($10 \times 7 \times 8p$)

Section 1 Test 4 (page 7)

1. conceal, show
2. temporary, permanent
3. descent, ascent
4. condemn, praise
5. assemble, disband
6. r (roar, red; floor, real)
7. t (sight, twist; start, trap)
8. l (steel, lost; school, lamb)
9. p (steep, pass; skip, prey)
10. s (class, sword; miss, swim)
11. WA (+4, +6)
12. XK (−5, −3)
13. BB (+6, −2)
14. TN (mirror code)
15. 7
16. 40/75 (or 8/15)

Section 1 Test 5 (page 8)

1. shop (I wi<u>sh op</u>portunities like that were more common!)
2. boat (Please place the gaze<u>bo at</u> the back of the garden.)
3. deep (The director ma<u>de ep</u>isodes for a daily show.)
4. pint (The dro<u>p in</u> temperature was unwelcome.)
5. tint (The little boy was accidentally shu<u>t in th</u>e cupboard.)
6. pales, peals
7. cares, races
8. times, items
9. coast, coats
10. stare, rates
11. 25 ($a \times b$)
12. 208 ($a \times b$)
13. 25 ($a \div b$)
14. 180 ($a \div b$)
15. 31
16. Monday

Section 1 Test 6 (page 9)

1. LOT (CLOTHES)
2. RUB (SCRUBBED)
3. RAY (STRAY)
4. ROT (TROTTED)
5. NEW (KNEW)
6. overhaul
7. headache
8. method
9. primate
10. poppies
11. 5
12. 37
13. 8
14. 2
15. 4
16. parcel 5 (order is 2, 4, 1, 3, 5 from heaviest to lightest)

Section 1 Test 7 (page 10)

1. enrage
2. horrific
3. stripey
4. militant
5. distress
6. chameleon, lizard (the others are amphibians)
7. xylophone, piano (the others are kitchen utensils)
8. book, guest (the others are places you visit)
9. path, bridleway (the others are for motor vehicles)
10. triangle, circle (the others are four-sided shapes)
11. mind
12. howl
13. tile
14. acts
15. PREDATOR
16. CREATIVE

Section 1 Test 8 (page 11)

1. bombard, pelt
2. habit, custom
3. prominent, outstanding
4. calm, soothe
5. upset, distress
6. GAME [TAME or GALE] [TIME or TALE] TILE
7. LICE [MICE or LACE] [MACE or MILE] MALE
8. WINE [WANE or SINE or WING] [SANE or SING] SANG
9. FILM [FILE] [PILE] PALE
10. WOOD [GOOD or WOAD] [GOAD] GOAT
11. HXIVVM (mirror code)
12. SCARF (−1 from code to word)
13. VOVEZGLI (mirror code)
14. HCDTKE (+2 from word to code)

15. 8.34 a.m./08:34
16. 6.37 p.m./18:37

Section 1 Test 9 (page 12)

1. safe
2. train
3. fan
4. band
5. fine
6. 4
7. 59
8. 45
9. 1
10. 100
11. BY (+1, −1)
12. LM (+2, +2)
13. NQ (leapfrogging −1, −2; +1, +1)
14. DN (first letter repeating pattern A, D, A, D, A; second letter +1)
15. C
16. 30

Section 1 Test 10 (page 13)

1. arrive, devoid (the others are synonyms for avoid)
2. tangerine, orange (the others are shades of brown)
3. gem, diamond (the others are precious metals)
4. industry, sufficient (the others are synonyms for defect)
5. axel, podium (the others are tools)
6. GOT (FORGOTTEN)
7. CAR (CARROTS)
8. SHE (WISHED)
9. WAR (WARNED)
10. LOW (FLOWED)
11. ZLXQ (−3 from word to code)
12. YLLPNZIP (mirror code)
13. HAIR (+1 from code to word)

14. QEOIYT (+4 from word to code)
15. 10 September
16. 13

Section 1 Test 11 (page 14)

1. liked, given (move n)
2. crate, shame (move first e)
3. rack, crumble (move first c)
4. sing, swerves (move w)
5. widow, never (move n)
6. E ([24 ÷ 8] × 5 = 15)
7. D ([1.5 × 3] + 1.5 = 6)
8. D (8 − [−1] = 9)
9. B ([14 × 3] − 31 = 11)
10. A ([18 − 12] × 5 = 30)
11. lead
12. row
13. loaf
14. pupil
15. 4
16. 18

Section 1 Test 12 (page 15)

1. conserve
2. straightforward
3. solid
4. delicate
5. let
6. a
7. t
8. e
9. y
10. d
11. noble
12. pasta
13. hare
14. olive
15. Clarence's father
16. Jana (from most to least Danny, Bren, Sarah, Shiv, Jana, Kim)

Section 2 Test 1
(page 16)

1. **73** (–12)
2. **0** (–8)
3. **406** (double it and add 10)
4. **40** (÷7 then 6 then 5, etc.)
5. **972** (×3)
6. screwdriver
7. pillowcase
8. increase
9. artwork
10. springboard
11. **96552**
12. **26185**
13. **65195**
14. LAPSE
15. C
16. **5** (Work out that 31 May is a Friday, and then work out the Saturdays in June: 1, 8, 15, 22, 29.)

Section 2 Test 2
(page 17)

1. coax
2. elude
3. scowl
4. fuse
5. scrape
6. **four, three** (Quad means four and tri means three.)
7. **explode, myth** (Explode is a synonym for erupt and myth is a synonym for fallacy)
8. **shirt, coat** (You hang a shirt on a hanger and a coat on a hook.)
9. **cygnet, eaglet** (A cygnet is a baby swan and an eaglet is a baby eagle.)
10. **lemon, lump** (Lemon is an anagram of melon and lump is an anagram of plum.)
11. **CW** (leapfrogging +2,+1)
12. **DZ** (–2, –2)
13. **!£*** (repeating pattern)
14. **VhR** (+2, +1, +1)
15. **72**
16. Saturday

Section 2 Test 3
(page 18)

1–5. *[score half a point for each correct answer]*
A = young animals
B = female animals
C = male animals
kid = A, bull = C ,
nanny = B, foal = A,
sow = B, stag = C,
billy = C, peahen = B,
gosling = A, doe = B
6. **C** (12 × 13 – 56 = 100)
7. **C** ([70 – 40] + 30 = 60)
8. **A** (7.5 + 0.5 – 2.5 = 5.5)
9. **D** (24 ÷ 12 + 18 = 20)
10. **E** ([125 – 57] – 45 = 23)
11. **ZV** (+7, +3)
12. **PX** (+5, –8)
13. **UB** (mirror code)
14. **AU** (–4, +3)
15. **16**
16. **7**

Section 2 Test 4
(page 19)

1. **disagree, reject** (the others are synonyms for consent)
2. **scales, ruler** (the others are synonyms for measure)
3. **distinguish, redistribute** (the others are synonyms for remember)
4. **classroom, blink** (the others are parts of the eye)
5. **speed, accelerate** (the others mean to move slowly)
6. clamber, climb
7. precise, exact
8. envious, jealous
9. rule, regulation
10. flicker, glimmer
11. jockey, horse, course
12. teacher, students, test
13. bananas, trees, countries
14. jury, verdict, trial
15. ELABORATE
16. EVOLUTION

Section 2 Test 5
(page 20)

1. **155** (a + b)
2. **68** (a + b + 5)
3. **10** (a – b + 10)
4. **5** (a – b ÷ 2)
5. **40** (a – b ÷ 4)
6. BEARD
7. ANGEL
8. TEARS
9. BAKER
10. LEAPT
11. **in** (Wolves are wild animals that hunt in packs.)
12. **yesterday** (I went to London Zoo on a school trip last week.)
13. **below** (The eagle swooped down suddenly from its perch.)
14. **is** (There are many different types of bird.)
15. sixth place
16. **whisk the eggs** (1. Measure milk 2. Mix sugar and butter 3. Turn on oven 4. Whisk eggs 5. Weigh flour)

Section 2 Test 6
(page 21)

1. DOME [HOME or DOPE] [HOPE] HOPS
2. LEAF [LEAD or DEAF] [DEAD] DEED
3. MIST [MAST or CIST] [CAST] CASE
4. BANG [HANG or BAND or BING] [HAND or BIND] HIND
5. WASP [WASH] [MASH] MUSH
6. grandparent
7. pickaxe
8. heartfelt
9. birdsong
10. foghorn
11. **O** (USRO**O**NME)
12. **N** (YTRR**N**IIGFE)
13. **N** (WRPO**N**MIGEE)

14. L (TPOML<u>I</u>EDCCA)
15. 42
16. 44

Section 2 Test 7
(page 22)

1. pins (The hunter laid the tra<u>p in s</u>ome haste.)
2. shin (We will look at it afre<u>sh in</u> a week.)
3. sown (Greg made the cake for hi<u>s own</u> party.)
4. face (After electing the chie<u>f a ce</u>lebration is held.)
5. band (The sorcerer gave the lamp a ru<u>b and</u> out popped a genie.)
6. root, plumb (move b)
7. hunt, alike (move a)
8. horn, sought (move s)
9. sale, cluck (move c)
10. olden, glower (move g)
11. p
12. t
13. b
14. l
15. 7.50 a.m./07:50
16. 12.12 p.m./12:12

Section 2 Test 8
(page 23)

1. giant
2. cowardly
3. plural
4. cramped
5. glossy
6. 5
7. 4
8. 950
9. 55
10. 19
11. apples, branches, tree
12. dentist, decay, patient's
13. athlete, jumping, hurdle
14. forecast, precipitation, duration
15. CONTROVERSY
16. EPIDEMIC

Section 2 Test 9
(page 24)

1. new, acorn (move a)
2. lash, rafts (move f)
3. pit, yearn (move n)
4. pie, plain (move second p)
5. leer, valley (move v)
6. repellent, hideous (the others are synonyms for attractive)
7. forget, fail (the others are synonyms for achieve)
8. argue, decry (the others are synonyms for joke)
9. clumsy, awkward (the others are synonyms for graceful)
10. tranquil, tender (the others are synonyms for fierce)
11. 600 (−100, −50 repeating pattern)
12. 130 (leapfrogging +30, +20 each time)
13. 69 (double and −1 each time)
14. 55 (add the two previous numbers)
15. 15 minutes and 4 seconds (lap 1: 3 mins 34 secs; lap 2: 3 mins 42 secs; lap 3: 3 mins 50 secs; lap 4: 3 mins 58 secs)
16. 8.25 a.m.

	Sets out	Time taken	Arrives
Mrs B	7.45 a.m.		9.25 a.m.
Mr T	7.50 a.m.		9.40 a.m.
Mr S	7.30 a.m.	55 mins	8.25 a.m.
Mr W			9.30 a.m.

Section 2 Test 10
(page 25)

1. oath (Did you know I have a pian<u>o at h</u>ome?)
2. slug (Please put Gemma'<u>s lug</u>gage in her room.)
3. down (The win<u>dow n</u>eeds to be shut.)
4. kiss (The tric<u>k is s</u>imple though it is difficult to disguise.)
5. work (Shall we call it a dra<u>w or k</u>eep playing?)
6. wholemeal
7. stopwatch
8. toothache
9. smartphone
10. laptop
11. 10 ([a + b] ÷ 4)
12. 5 ([a ÷ b] + 1) or (a + b) ÷ b
13. 49 ([a + b] + 10)
14. 50 ([a − b] + 10)
15. OUTRAGEOUS
16. MAGNIFIED

Section 2 Test 11
(page 26)

1. pin
2. male
3. dale
4. sail
5. meal
6. ATE (DATE)
7. RIP (TRIPPED)
8. PEA (PEAK)
9. DUE (DUEL)
10. ASK (MASKS)
11. O X (leapfrogging +1, −2; −1 −2)
12. U V (+5, +5)
13. D E (+3, +3)
14. I J (+2, +2)
15. 4 (Find all the Saturdays in March: 12, 19, 26. There are 31 days in March so the last day of March is a Thursday, so 1 April will be a Friday. The first Monday is 4 April and the rest of the Mondays are 11, 18, 25.)
16. 26 May

Answers

Section 2 Test 12 (page 27)

1. NE (+7, +1)
2. YB (−2, +6)
3. IF (mirror code)
4. CX (−3, −5)
5. XA (mirror code)
6. and, dropped (I *dropped* my phone *and* its screen broke.)
7. the, 26 (There are *26* letters in *the* alphabet.)
8. lotion, must (You *must* wear *lotion* when it's sunny.)
9. the, blowing (The washing was *blowing* in *the* breeze.)
10. race, exciting (There was an *exciting* finish to the *race*.)
11. flower
12. creak
13. amuse
14. raid
15. Jess
16. Brian

Section 3 Test 1 (page 28)

1–5. *[score half a point for each correct answer]*
    A = language
    B = country
    C = city
    Spanish = A, England = B,
    Oslo = C, Paris = C,
    Urdu = A, Pakistan = B,
    Australia = B, Peru = B,
    Madrid = C, Cantonese = A
6. rage (I made the seller <u>a ge</u>nerous offer.)
7. lane (My friend asked me to seal <u>an e</u>nvelope for him.)
8. kind (Firemen will kic<u>k in d</u>oors when they cannot get through another way.)
9. fort (The treasure is either at the bottom of the clif<u>f or t</u>he bottom of the sea.)
10. lamb ("Please don't s<u>lam b</u>ooks onto the counter" urged the librarian.)

11. GKOQ (+1 +2 +3, etc. from word to code)
12. ELRXV (mirror code)
13. QVDVO (mirror code)
14. CYAN (−1 −2 −3 etc. from code to word)
15. 20/55 = 4/11
16. 12/48 = 1/4

Section 3 Test 2 (page 29)

1. 29 (a + b − 1)
2. 5 (a ÷ b + 1)
3. 4 (a ÷ b + 2)
4. 91 (a × b +1)
5. 34 (a × b + 2)
6. CYCLE
7. MOWER
8. TOAST
9. KNIFE
10. PLANTS
11. EAT (SWEAT)
12. URN (FURNITURE)
13. OAT (LOATHES)
14. SEA (DISEASE)
15. 4.40 p.m./16:40
16. 10 800 seconds

Section 3 Test 3 (page 30)

1. race, time (What *time* does the swimming *race* start today?)
2. unsuspecting, prowled (The cat *prowled* silently towards the *unsuspecting* mouse.)
3. rocks, waves (The *waves* crashed loudly against the jagged *rocks*.)
4. over, threw (My baby sister *threw* her lunch *over* the side of her highchair.)
5. night, audience (There was a large *audience* at the last *night* of the play.)
6. 12
7. 37
8. 0.2
9. 6

10. 3
11. 7236
12. 87226
13. 87932
14. TWINS
15. roses (order is chrysanthemums, irises, carnations, poppies, lilies, daffodils, roses)
16. Tristan (order from oldest to youngest is Yanek, Luka, Mack, Sven, Tristan)

Section 3 Test 4 (page 31)

1. L (EEILSUV)
2. R (DEIRSSST)
3. D (ACCDEEPT)
4. N (DEINRRTU)
5. E (BCCEILY)
6. YQ (−8, +4)
7. DV (+5, +3)
8. GK (mirror code)
9. EC (−7, +4)
10. WN (mirror code)
11. may
12. down
13. key
14. in
15. 16 in 48 = 1/3
16. 3:2 (24:16 = 6:4 = 3:2)

Section 3 Test 5 (page 32)

1. robe, prove (move p)
2. fight, friends (move r)
3. water, brain (move i)
4. soot, chopped (move c) or coot, shopped (move s)
5. same, through (move h)
6. rehearse
7. seek
8. emerge
9. rabble
10. wick
11. OB (first letter −4, −3, −2, −1; second letter +1, +2, +3, +4)
12. =+@= (repeating pattern)

13. QYz (first letter +1; second letter +1; third letter −1)
14. AR (leapfrogging first letter −2; second letter −1)
15. Milo (order from oldest to youngest Paulo, Asha, Manesh/Dev, Will, Milo)
16. Mel

Section 3 Test 6 (page 33)

1. aptitude, ability
2. retrieve, fetch
3. evade, avoid
4. lanky, skinny
5. define, classify
6. magnet
7. silver
8. trauma
9. beneficial
10. amaze
11. UFGFIV (mirror code)
12. HAMMER (+1, +0, +1, +0, etc. from code to word)
13. ZRLY (−1, −0, −1, −0 from word to code)
14. COMB (mirror code)
15. 22 August
16. 1933

Section 3 Test 7 (page 34)

1. book
2. work (accept fire)
3. any (accept some)
4. water
5. under
6. n
7. f
8. h
9. c
10. g
11. land (What type of f<u>lan d</u>o you like best?)

12. halo (I wis<u>h a lo</u>t more people were kind like you! NB: 'a lot' is two words, so cannot be the correct answer.)
13. teas (She isn't as poli<u>te as</u> my sister.)
14. wand (The c<u>ow and</u> the dog laughed as the dish ran away with the spoon.)
15. 1461 (as one of the years will be a leap year)
16. 08:21

Section 3 Test 8 (page 35)

1. 50 ([a + b] ÷ 2)
2. 47 (a + b + 2)
3. 235 (a × b)
4. 80 (b ÷ a)
5. 42 (a × b + a) or (a × [b + 1])
6. safe, hazardous
7. careful, reckless
8. timid, bold
9. pedestrian, motorist
10. ancient, modern
11. LOST [<u>LAST</u> or <u>COST</u>] [<u>CAST</u>] CASE
12. SAME [<u>LAME</u>] [<u>LAMP</u> or <u>LIME</u>] LIMP
13. ROAM [<u>ROAD</u>] [<u>TOAD</u>] TOLD
14. BILE [<u>BALE</u>] [<u>BALM</u>] CALM
15. 6.45 p.m./18:45
16. 4.24 p.m./16:24

Section 3 Test 9 (page 36)

1. sinister
2. disaster
3. answer
4. irritate
5. recall
6. changeable, rickety
7. witch, duchess
8. foal, gosling
9. aromatic, savage

10. course, symbol (homophones)
11. grid
12. some
13. balm
14. sire
15. 40
16. 96 (The pink and the red box each have 48 green bricks.)

Section 3 Test 10 (page 37)

1. B ([36 × 2] ÷ 6 = 12)
2. C ([180 ÷ 6] + 56 = 86)
3. A (78 + 92 + 40 = 210)
4. C ([24 × 4] − 16 = 80)
5. D ([400 ÷ 5] − 54 = 26)
6. bridge, arc (the others are types of boat)
7. sensible, silly (the others mean unable to speak)
8. prise, lever (the others mean to value something highly)
9. fake, reel (the others are synonyms for genuine)
10. melody, jealousy (the others are synonyms for sadness)
11. KP (mirror code)
12. JK (−4, +8)
13. IT (+7, −7)
14. UB (mirror code)
15. £1 and 5p coins
16. 2.05 kg

Answers

Section 3 Test 11 (page 38)

1. **magnify, amplify** (Microscopes magnify things and microphones amplify sounds.)
2. **careless, superior** (Careless is a synonym for reckless and superior is a synonym for arrogant.)
3. **contest, fowl** (Contest is a synonym for tournament and fowl is a synonym for bird.)
4. **spins, stool** (Spins is snips spelt backwards and stool is loots spelt backwards.)
5. **chaos, usual** (Chaos is the opposite of order and usual is the opposite of peculiar.)
6. **25** (+3, +5, +7, +9, +11)
7. **–12** (+6)
8. **–2** (repeating pattern +2 –4)
9. **7.5** (÷2)
10. **25** (repeating pattern –25 –15)
11. r
12. w
13. h
14. n
15. 16
16. **8** (4 pairs)

Section 3 Test 12 (page 39)

1. **100**
2. **0**
3. **87**
4. **90**
5. **4**
6. attract, repel
7. live, dead
8. flawless, blemished
9. fertile, barren
10. youthful, aged
11. **9718**
12. **5183**
13. **9319**
14. OFFER
15. C
16. E

This book of answers is a pull-out section from
Rapid Reasoning Tests: Verbal Reasoning 5

Published by Schofield & Sims Ltd,
Dogley Mill, Fenay Bridge, Huddersfield HD8 0NQ, UK
Telephone 01484 607080
www.schofieldandsims.co.uk

Copyright © Schofield & Sims Ltd, 2014

Author: **Siân Goodspeed**. Siân Goodspeed has asserted her moral right under the Copyright, Designs and Patents Act, 1988, to be identified as the author of this work.

British Library Cataloguing in Publication Data. A catalogue record for this book is available from the British Library.

Commissioned by **Carolyn Richardson Publishing Services** (www.publiserve.co.uk)

Design by **Oxford Designers & Illustrators**
Printed in India by **Multivista Global Ltd**

ISBN 978 07217 1242 0

Target time: **10 minutes**

Change the first word into the last word. Only change **one** letter at a time, making two new four-letter words in the middle. Write the new words.

Example TRAP [_TRAM_][_PRAM_]PROM

1. DOME [_____][_____]HOPS
2. LEAF [_____][_____]DEED
3. MIST [_____][_____]CASE
4. BANG [_____][_____]HIND
5. WASP [_____][_____]MUSH

Underline the **two** words, one from each group, that together make one new word. The word from the first group comes first.

Example (<u>drain</u>, gutter, ditch)   (rain, <u>pipe</u>, flow)   (drainpipe)

6. (grand, fancy, ornate)   (tree, family, parent)
7. (choose, choice, pick)   (sword, axe, grip)
8. (heart, blood, body)   (more, felt, even)
9. (bird, fly, robin)   (music, song, strong)
10. (mist, fog, wave)   (noise, blow, horn)

If the letters in each word were listed in **reverse alphabetical order**, which letter would come **fifth**? Write the answer on the line.

Example IMAGINE __G__ (NMIIGEA)

1. ENORMOUS ____
2. TERRIFYING ____
13. EMPOWERING ____
14. COMPLICATED ____

Work out the answers. Write your answers on the lines.

5. Jamie is **20** and his brother is **18**. Jamie's mother is twice Jamie's age now. How old will Jamie's mother be when Jamie's brother is **20**? _____

6. I feed my cat Sally with **3** tins of food a day. My brother feeds his cat Graham with $2\frac{1}{2}$ tins of food a day. How many tins of food will Sally and Graham eat between them in **8** days?

_____

End of test.

Score:		Time taken:		Target met?	

Find the **four-letter word** hidden across two or more consecutive words in each sentence below. The order of the letters must stay the same. Underline the word and write it on the line.

Example How many cakes have you ea<u>ten t</u>oday?   <u>tent</u>

1. The hunter laid the trap in some haste. _____
2. We will look at it afresh in a week. _____
3. Greg made the cake for his own party. _____
4. After electing the chief a celebration is held. _____
5. The sorcerer gave the lamp a rub and out popped a genie. _____

Move one letter from the first word to the second word to make two new words. Write he two new words on the lines.

Example liver, down   <u>live</u> , <u>drown</u>   (move the r)

6. robot, plum   _____ , _____
7. haunt, like   _____ , _____
8. shorn, ought   _____ , _____

9. scale, luck   _____ , _____
10. golden, lower   _____ , _____

Find **one** missing letter that completes **both** pairs of words. Write it on the lines.

Example truc [_k_] ite   lic [_k_] now

11. cree [__] lank   stoo [__] each
12. scoo [__] wist   stru [__] end

13. stu [__] eat   cra [__] rain
14. cur [__] eer   meta [__] oom

Work out the answers. Write your answers on the lines.

15. Moseeb has to get to the train station in time for the **8.35** a.m. train. It takes him **25** minutes to get himself ready and then **20** minutes to walk to the station. What time does he need to get up in order to get to the station on time? _____

16. Cath and Simon are baking cakes for the school summer fete. The cakes require **15** minutes of preparation time, then **12** minutes baking plus **10** minutes to cool down on the wire rack before they can put them into the box to transport. If they start making the cakes at **11.35** a.m., what time will they be ready to go? _____

End of test

Score:	Time taken:	Target met?

Underline the word in brackets that is most **opposite** in meaning to the word in capitals.

Example BEAUTIFUL   (fair, <u>ugly</u>, pretty, graceful)

1. MINUSCULE   (giant, miniature, dwindle, dawdle)
2. COURAGEOUS   (considerate, powerful, cowardly, assured)
3. SINGULAR   (solitary, peculiar, plural, alone)
4. SPACIOUS   (scornful, splendid, crescent, cramped)
5. DULL   (glum, deep, glossy, dim, boring)

Find the missing number in each equation. Write it on the line.

Example 4 + 3 = 2 + ___5___

6. (240 ÷ 8) + 20 = 40 + 15 – _____
7. 98 × 2 = 200 – _____
8. 350 × 3 = 2000 – _____
9. 1000 – 400 – 25 = 500 + 20 + _____
10. (49 ÷ 7) + 8 = 34 – _____

Underline **one** word in each set of brackets to complete the sentence best.

Example The bus (wheels, <u>conductor</u>, passenger) collected the (food, <u>fares</u>, ride) from the (<u>passengers</u>, babies, driver).

11. The (grapes, apples, carrots) were hanging from the (trunk, branches, leaves) of the (flower, pip, tree).
12. The (magician, physicist, dentist) removed the (rabbit, decay, wand) from the (patient's, audience's, crowd's) mouth.
13. The (athlete, ballerina, actor) injured herself (performing, jumping, running) over the (hurdle, stage, show).
14. The weather (clouds, forecast, rain) predicted light (punctuation, precipitation, sunshine) for the (year, duration, event) of the match.

Use the word's definition to help you fill in the missing letters.

Example G <u>E</u> N E <u>R</u> <u>O</u> US giving, charitable   (GENEROUS)

15. C O N __ R __ V __ R S __   debate, disagreement, dispute
16. E P __ __ __ E M __ C outbreak, plague, scourge

End of test.

Score: | Time taken: | Target met?

■ Move one letter from the first word to the second word to make two new words. Write the two new words on the lines.

Example liver, down	_____live_____ , _____drown_____ (move the r)

1. anew, corn _____ , _____

2. flash, rats _____ , _____

3. pint, year _____ , _____

4. pipe, lain _____ , _____

5. lever, alley _____ , _____

■ In each group, three words go together and two are the odd ones out. Underline the **two** words that do **not** go with the other three.

Example comprehend   understand   <u>confuse</u>   <u>unsure</u>   grasp

6. repellent   alluring   attractive   tempting   hideous

7. achieve   accomplish   realise   forget   fail

8. joke   argue   jape   jest   decry

9. clumsy   graceful   elegant   refined   awkward

10. ferocious   tranquil   fierce   savage   tender

■ Find the missing number in each sequence. Write it on the line.

Example 20   22   24   26   28   __30__   (+2 each time)

11. 900   800   750   650   _____   500   450

12. 40   20   70   40   100   60   _____

13. 18   35   _____   137   273

14. 13   21   34   _____   89   144

■ Work out the answers. Write your answers on the lines.

15. It takes Ben 3 minutes 34 seconds to jog round the perimeter of the park the first time. Each consecutive time, he slows down by 8 seconds. By the time he completes his fourth lap of the park, how long will it have taken him altogether? _____

16. Four colleagues are travelling to a conference. Mr T leaves home 5 minutes after Mrs B who sets off 15 minutes later than Mr S. Mr S takes 55 minutes to get to the conference. Mr W arrives at the conference at 9.30 a.m., 10 minutes before Mr T. Mrs B leaves home at 7.45 a.m. and arrives 5 minutes before Mr W. What time does Mr S arrive at the conference? _____

End of test

Score:		Time taken:		Target met?	

Find the **four-letter word** hidden across two or more consecutive words in each sentence below. The order of the letters must stay the same. Underline the word and write it on the line.

Example How many cakes have you ea<u>ten</u> today?   <u>tent</u>

1. Did you know I have a piano at home? _____

2. Please put Gemma's luggage in her room. _____

3. The window needs to be shut. _____

4. The trick is simple though it is difficult to disguise. _____

5. Shall we call it a draw or keep playing? _____

Underline the **two** words, one from each group, that together make one new word. The word from the first group comes first.

Example (<u>drain</u>, gutter, ditch)   (rain, <u>pipe</u>, flow)   (drainpipe)

6. (gap, hole, whole)   (meal, strike, punch)

7. (halt, stop, catch)   (race, watch, look)

8. (teeth, tooth, molar)   (hurt, ache, pain)

9. (clever, smart, new)   (phone, teach, light)

10. (hip, stomach, lap)   (below, above, top)

Work out the missing number and write it on the line.

Example 3 [5] 2   4 [6] 2   5 [_8_] 3
(a + b = ?, where a represents the number on the left and b represents the number on the right)

1. 2 [3] 10   40 [12] 8   39 [_____] 1

2. 18 [3] 9   24 [3] 12   40 [_____] 10

3. 33 [58] 15   19 [70] 41   22 [_____] 17

4. 108 [110] 8   46 [43] 13   75 [_____] 35

Use the word's definition to help you fill in the missing letters.

Example G <u>E</u> N E R <u>O</u> US   giving, charitable   (GENEROUS)

5. O __ T R __ G __ __ U S   shocking, extravagant, offensive

6. M A __ __ I __ __ E D   exaggerated, overstated, enlarged

End of test.

Score:	Time taken:	Target met?

■ Make a new word by changing the first word of the third pair in the same way as the other pairs. Write the new word on the line.

> **Example** crook, rock cloak, lock sport, ____post____ (take the 2nd, 3rd, 1st, 5th letters)

1. stain, sin brain, bin plain, _____
2. love, vole pore, rope lame, _____
3. leaves, sale staple, east leaned, _____
4. breath, hear bleach, heal flails, _____
5. elevate, veal climate, meal plumage, _____

■ In each of the sentences below, the word in capitals has three letters missing. Those three letters spell a word. Write the three-letter word on the line.

> **Example** The baby **DK** her milk from the bottle. ____RAN____ (DRANK)

6. The **D** of the wedding was 26 July. _____
7. She **TPED** on the stairs. _____
8. The mountain had the highest **K**. _____
9. The two swordsmen had a **L**. _____
10. At the fancy dress ball, everyone wore **MS**. _____

■ Find the missing letter pair in the sequence. Write it on the line. Use the alphabet to help you.

A B C D E F G H I J K L M N O P Q R S T U V W X Y Z

> **Example** RS UV XY AB __DE__ (+3, +3)

11. LD FC MB EA NZ DY _____   13. XY AB _____ GH JK
12. AB FG KL PQ _____   14. AB CD EF GH _____

■ Work out the answers. Write your answers on the lines.

15. How many Mondays are there in April if **5 March** is a Saturday? _____
16. Mel is going on holiday for **10 nights**. If she returns home on **5 June**, what date did her holiday start? _____

End of test

Score:		Time taken:		Target met?	

Target time: 10 minutes

Using the alphabet to help you, find the letter pair that completes each sentence. Write it on the line.

A B C D E F G H I J K L M N O P Q R S T U V W X Y Z

Example **XY** is to **TU** as **NO** is to ___JK___. (−4, −4)

1. **TY** is to **AZ** as **GD** is to _____.
2. **CW** is to **AC** as **AV** is to _____.
3. **EL** is to **VO** as **RU** is to _____.
4. **BW** is to **YR** as **FC** is to _____.
5. **GR** is to **TI** as **CZ** is to _____.

Underline the **two** words in each sentence that need to change places in order for the sentence to make sense.

Example Where do you <u>to</u> <u>go</u> school?   (Where do you <u>go</u> <u>to</u> school?)

6. I and my phone dropped its screen broke.
7. There are the letters in 26 alphabet.
8. You lotion wear must when it's sunny.
9. The washing was the in blowing breeze.
10. There was an race finish to the exciting.

Underline the word in brackets that is **closest** in meaning to the word in capitals.

Example LUCKY   (unlucky, <u>fortunate</u>, kind, helpful)

11. BLOOM   (crash, flower, explode, budding)
12. GROAN   (creek, creak, roam, cheer)
13. ENTERTAIN   (show, master, amuse, applaud)
14. FORAY   (accuse, forgive, venture, raid)

Work out the answers. Write your answers on the lines.

15. Scott's friends are comparing how much pocket money their parents give them. Hugo gets more money than Jess, who gets more money than Paige. Scott is jealous of Fred because Fred gets the most money. Tilly does not get as much money as Jess, but she does get more than Paige. Guido and Scott do not get any pocket money. Who gets the third most money? _____

16. It is sports day at Gina's school. She is taking part in the long jump with four of her friends. Gina jumps further than Sal, who jumps further than Mo but not as far as Jake. Brian jumps further than Jake. Gina finishes in third place. Who jumped the furthest? _____

End of test.

Score:		Time taken:		Target met?	

1–5. Look at the words in groups A, B and C. For each of the words below, choose the correct group and write its letter on the line.

A	B	C
French	Germany	Sydney

Spanish _____   England _____   Oslo _____   Paris _____   Urdu _____

Pakistan _____   Australia _____   Peru _____   Madrid _____   Cantonese _____

Find the **four-letter word** hidden across two or more consecutive words in each sentence below. The order of the letters must stay the same. Underline the word and write it on the line.

Example How many cakes have you ea<u>ten</u> today?   <u>   tent   </u>

6. I made the seller a generous offer. _____

7. My friend asked me to seal an envelope for him. _____

8. Firemen will kick in doors when they cannot get through another way. _____

9. The treasure is either at the bottom of the cliff or the bottom of the sea. _____

10. "Please don't slam books onto the counter" urged the librarian. _____

Using the alphabet to help you, crack the code. Write your answer on the line.

A B C D E F G H I J K L M N O P Q R S T U V W X Y Z

Example If the code for **TOP** is **UPQ**, what is the code for **TIP**?   <u> UJQ </u>

(+1 from word to code)

11. If the code for **VIDEO** is **WKGIT**, what is the code for **FILM**? _____

12. If **MAGICAL** is written in code as **NZTRXZO**, what is the code for **VOICE**? _____

13. If the code for **EARRING** is **VZIIRMT**, what is the code for **JEWEL**? _____

14. If the code **CNXI** means **BLUE**, what does the code **DADR** mean? _____

Work out the answers. Write your answers on the lines.

15. If there are **20** green grapes and **35** red grapes in a punnet, what proportion of all the grapes are green? _____

16. There are **48** sweets in a jar. If **12** of them are toffees, what is the probability of Lacey selecting a toffee if she picks a sweet out without looking? _____

End of test.

Score:	Time taken:	Target met?

Target time: 10 minutes

Work out the missing number and write it on the line.

Example 3 [5] 2   4 [6] 2   5 [__8__] 3
(a + b = ?, where a represents the number on the left and b represents the number on the right)

1. 19 [39] 21   10 [29] 20   13 [_____] 17   4. 9 [37] 4   12 [145] 12   10 [_____] 9
2. 20 [3] 10   40 [6] 8   20 [_____] 5   5. 12 [50] 4   10 [92] 9   8 [_____] 4
3. 21 [5] 7   15 [5] 5   18 [_____] 9

Rearrange the letters in capitals to make a new word so that the sentence makes sense. Write the new word on the line.

Example The **NUS** shone brightly. _____SUN_____

6. The boys rode along the **CLECY** path as fast as they could. _____
7. Dad got out of cutting the lawn by saying the **WMORE** would not start. _____
8. Charlotte liked to have **OTATS** for her breakfast on a school day. _____
9. The **FKNIE** used for the bread was hung out of reach. _____
10. Grandad transferred the **TSALNP** to larger pots so they could grow bigger. _____

In each of the sentences below, the word in capitals has three letters missing. Those three letters spell a word. Write the three-letter word on the line.

Example The baby **DK** her milk from the bottle. _____RAN_____ (DRANK)

11. Running made the athletes **SW**. _____
12. He loaded the **FITURE** onto the removal lorry. _____
13. My dog **LHES** cats so he barks at them. _____
14. My friend caught a tropical **DISE** while on holiday. _____

Work out the answers. Write your answers on the lines.

15. Mrs Speed takes **45** minutes in the supermarket to do her shopping. It takes her **15** minutes to get to the shop and find a parking space. She then takes **25** minutes to get back home through the rush hour traffic. She arrives back home at **6.05** p.m. What time did she set out? _____

16. How many seconds are there in 3 hours? _____

End of test.

Score:		Time taken:		Target met?	

Target time: **10 minutes**

■ Underline the **two** words in each sentence that need to change places in order for the sentence to make sense.

> **Example** Where do you <u>to</u> <u>go</u> school?   (Where do you <u>go</u> <u>to</u> school?)

1. What race does the swimming time start today?
2. The cat unsuspecting silently towards the prowled mouse.
3. The rocks crashed loudly against the jagged waves.
4. My baby sister over her lunch threw the side of her highchair.
5. There was a large night at the last audience of the play.

■ Find the missing number in each equation. Write it on the line.

> **Example** $4 + 3 = 2 + \underline{5}$

6. $(190 \div 10) \times 2 = (250 \div 5) - \underline{}$
7. $4^3 = 3^3 + \underline{}$
8. $220 \div 11 = 100 \times \underline{}$
9. $3^3 \times 2^3 = 6 \times \underline{}$
10. $78 \div 2 = 6^2 + \underline{}$

■ Match the number codes to the words. One code is missing. Use these to help you work out the answers to the questions. Write your answers on the lines.

NEWT   TWIST   WEST   TWINE   67932   67986   7286

What is the code for:

11. **WENT**? _____   12. **SWEET**? _____   13. **SWINE**? _____
14. What does the code **67938** mean? _____

■ Work out the answers. Write your answers on the lines.

15. Sylvia displays vases of flowers in a row outside her florist shop. She puts the daffodils between the roses and the lilies. The carnations are next to the irises which are also next to the chrysanthemums. The poppies are between the lilies and the carnations. The chrysanthemums are at one end of the row. Which flowers are at the other end of the row? _____

16. Yanek is older than Tristan who is younger than Sven. Mack is younger than Luka but older than Sven. Yanek is the oldest. Who is the youngest? _____

End of test

Score:		Time taken:		Target met?	

Target time: 10 minutes

If the letters in each word were listed in alphabetical order, which letter would come **fourth**? Write the answer on the line.

Example IMAGINE __I__ (AEGIIMN)

1. ELUSIVE ____
2. DISTRESS ____
3. ACCEPTED ____

4. INTRUDER ____
5. BICYCLE ____

Using the alphabet to help you, find the letter pair that completes each sentence. Write it on the line.

A B C D E F G H I J K L M N O P Q R S T U V W X Y Z

Example **XY** is to **TU** as **NO** is to __JK__. (−4, −4)

6. **BY** is to **TC** as **GM** is to _____.
7. **QP** is to **VS** as **YS** is to _____.
8. **JS** is to **QH** as **TP** is to _____.

9. **UD** is to **NH** as **LY** is to _____.
10. **OT** is to **LG** as **DM** is to _____.

Each word below can be changed into a new word by putting another word in **front**. The added word should be the **same** for each word in the row. Find the word and write it on the line.

Example brush dresser piece style ____hair____

11. pole hem be flower _____
12. side fall hill right _____
13. note board hole pad _____
14. mate come to doors _____

Work out the answers. Write your answers on the lines.

15. What is the probability of selecting a green sock from a bag containing 11 pairs of red socks, 5 pairs of blue socks and 8 pairs of green socks? _____

16. In an orchard, there are 24 apple trees, 16 pear trees and 12 plum trees. What is the ratio of apple to pear trees in its simplest form? _____

End of test.

| Score: | | Time taken: | | Target met? | |

Target time: **10 minutes**

 Move one letter from the first word to the second word to make two new words. Write the two new words on the lines.

> **Example** liver, down _____live_____ , _____drown_____ (move the r)

1. probe, rove _____ , _____
2. fright, fiends _____ , _____
3. waiter, bran _____ , _____

4. scoot, hopped _____ , _____
5. shame, trough _____ , _____

■ Underline the word in the first group that goes best with the three words in brackets.

> **Example** <u>assist</u>, hinder, try (help, aid, support)

6. relieve, release, rehearse (practise, prepare, train)
7. send, seek, lose (search, pursue, hunt)
8. emerge, diverge, divulge (materialise, surface, appear)
9. rubble, stone, rabble (crowd, throng, mob)
10. wick, wire, switch (candle, wax, flame)

■ Find the missing letters or symbols in the sequence. Write them on the line. Use the alphabet to help you.

A B C D E F G H I J K L M N O P Q R S T U V W X Y Z

> **Example** RS UV XY AB __DE__ (+3, +3)

11. YR US RU PX _____
12. @=+@ =+@= +@=+ @=+@ _____
13. PXa _____ RZy SAx TBw
14. GU MR ET OT CS QV _____ SX

■ Work out the answers. Write your answers on the lines.

15. Paulo is older than Manesh. Manesh and Dev are the same age. Asha is younger than Paulo but older than Manesh. Will is younger than Dev but older than Milo. Who is the youngest?

_____

16. There are five children on a roundabout. Justin is to Jade's left. Sabine is to Robyn's right. Mel is not next to Jade. Who is to the right of Sabine? _____

End of tes

Score:		Time taken:		Target met?	

Target time: 10 minutes

Underline the pair of words that are most **similar** in meaning.

Example (rain, snow)   (sea, sand)   (earth, mud)

1. (aptitude, ability)   (grant, take)   (inept, skilful)
2. (liken, like)   (retrieve, fetch)   (conclude, concern)
3. (vocation, holiday)   (evade, avoid)   (invasion, escape)
4. (lanky, skinny)   (tense, relaxed)   (attract, repel)
5. (absorb, abstain)   (enlarge, shrink)   (define, classify)

If these words were listed in alphabetical order, which word would come **second**? Write the answer on the line.

Example drink drain dire driver drawn   _____drawn_____

6. magnificent   magnet   magnify   magnate   majesty   _____
7. silent   solvent   solution   solitude   silver   _____
8. tractor   triceps   trauma   travel   traveller   _____
9. benefit   benefactor   beneficial   benevolent   benefitting   _____
0. astound   amaze   alter   asteroid   amiable   _____

Using the alphabet to help you, crack the code. Write your answer on the line.

A B C D E F G H I J K L M N O P Q R S T U V W X Y Z

Example If the code for **TOP** is **UPQ**, what is the code for **TIP**?   _____UJQ_____

(+ 1 from word to code)

1. If the code for **PRESENT** is **KIVHVMG**, what is the code for **FUTURE**? _____
2. If the code **RHDLUER** means **SHELVES**, what does the code **GALMDR** mean? _____
3. If the code for **DESK** is **CERK**, what is the code for **ARMY**? _____
4. If the code **YVZIW** means **BEARD**, what does the code **XLNY** mean? _____

Work out the answers. Write your answers on the lines.

5. In 3 weeks and 2 days, it will be my birthday. If my birthday is 14 September, what is the date today? _____

6. In 2011, Jenny's grandfather celebrated his 78th birthday. In what year was he born?
_____

End of test.

Score:	Time taken:	Target met?

↓
■ Each word below can be changed into a new word by putting another word in **front**. The added word should be the **same** for each word in the row. Find the word and write it on the line.

Example brush   dresser   piece   style   ___hair___

1. keeper   case   mark   worm   _____
2. place   station   man   house   _____
3. one   body   how   where   _____
4. front   way   fall   works   _____
5. clothes   statement   hand   growth   _____

■ Find **one** missing letter that completes **both** pairs of words. Write it on the lines.

Example truc [_k_] ite   lic [_k_] now

6. gai [__] ick   brow [__] urse
7. gruf [__] irst   snif [__] eat
8. sig [__] eel   trut [__] asty

9. publi [__] hief   atti [__] ared
10. slin [__] reet   shru [__] lee

■ Find the **four-letter word** across two or more consecutive words in each sentence below. The order of the letters must stay the same. Underline the word and write it on the line.

Example How many cakes have you ea<u>ten </u>today?   ___tent___

11. What type of flan do you like best?   _____
12. I wish a lot more people were kind like you!   _____
13. She isn't as polite as my sister.   _____
14. The cow and the dog laughed as the dish ran away with the spoon.   _____

■ Work out the answers. Write your answers on the lines.

15. How many days are there in 4 years?   _____
16. The **07:52** bus from New Town to Old Town usually takes **24** minutes to complete its journey. However, on Monday it was **5** minutes late leaving New Town. What time did it arrive in Old Town?

_____

End of test

Score:		Time taken:		Target met?	

Target time: 10 minutes

Work out the missing number and write it on the line.

Example 3 [5] 2   4 [6] 2   5 [_8_] 3
(a + b = ?, where a represents the number on the left and b represents the number on the right)

1. 30 [25] 20   100 [100] 100   80 [_____] 20
2. 17 [151] 132   6 [18] 10   42 [_____] 3
3. 38 [152] 4   29 [87] 3   47 [_____] 5
4. 7 [30] 210   4 [90] 360   5 [_____] 400
5. 12 [48] 3   13 [39] 2   14 [_____] 2

Underline the **two** words, one from each group, that are most **opposite** in meaning.

Example (<u>old</u>, son, home)   (<u>new</u>, grandfather, house)

6. (safe, gradual, hasty)   (hazardous, hideous, heaped)
7. (cheerful, careful, breathless)   (reckless, caress, cautious)
8. (timed, trim, timid)   (bald, bold, shy)
9. (pedestrian, pedestal, traveller)   (engineer, motorist, jockey)
0. (technology, museum, ancient)   (culture, modern, childish)

Change the first word into the last word. Only change **one** letter at a time, making two new four-letter words in the middle. Write the new words.

Example TRAP [_TRAM_][_PRAM_] PROM

1. LOST [_____][_____] CASE   13. ROAM [_____][_____] TOLD
2. SAME [_____][_____] LIMP   14. BILE [_____][_____] CALM

Work out the answers. Write your answers on the lines.

5. Brendon is performing in a concert at **8.15** p.m. He needs to arrive **30** minutes before the concert begins at **8** p.m. and it takes him **35** minutes to travel to the hall by bus. Buses leave on the hour and then every **15** minutes from outside Brendon's house. Which bus does Brendon need to get to ensure he arrives on time? _____

5. Judy's watch is 11 minutes fast. If her watch says the time is **4.35** p.m., what time is it really?
_____

End of test.

Score:	Time taken:	Target met?

■ Underline the word in the first group that goes best with the three words in brackets.

> **Example** <u>assist</u>, hinder, try   (help, aid, support)

1. deadly, sinister, murky   (eerie, unsettling, chilling)
2. disaster, capacity, frailty   (catastrophe, calamity, tragedy)
3. query, remark, answer   (respond, reply, retort)
4. irritate, mistake, sadden   (vex, annoy, irk)
5. replay, recall, relay   (remember, recollect, recount)

■ Underline the **two** words, one from each group, that will complete the sentence in the best way.

> **Example** **Mother** is to (lady, home, <u>daughter</u>) as **father** is to (<u>son</u>, old, beard).

6. **Fixed** is to (changeable, certain, single) as **stable** is to (horse, rickety, sensible).
7. **Wizard** is to (which, witch, wicked) as **duke** is to (damsel, heiress, duchess).
8. **Horse** is to (calf, kid, foal) as **goose** is to (gosling, duckling, chick).
9. **Fragrant** is to (odour, aromatic, perfume) as **barbaric** is to (suave, courageous, savage).
10. **Coarse** is to (rough, smooth, course) as **cymbal** is to (crash, symbol, beat).

■ Make a new word by changing the first word of the third pair in the same way as the other pairs. Write the new word on the line.

> **Example** crook, rock   cloak, lock   sport, ____post____   (take the 2nd, 3rd, 1st, 5th letters)

11. booth, hoot   heart, tear   bridge, _____   13. erase, ears   slats, salt   blame, _____
12. tease, sate   shore, rose   moose, _____   14. talent, late   litter, tilt   risen, _____

■ Work out the answers. Write your answers on the lines.

15. Calvin is bird-watching. 10% of the birds he sees are woodpeckers. He sees twice as many blackbirds as woodpeckers. He sees 12 pigeons, 16 sparrows and 8 blackbirds. How many birds does Calvin see altogether? _____

16. In a nursery, there are 4 boxes of coloured bricks. In the pink box, there are 3:2 green to yellow bricks. In the orange box, there are 4:1 red to blue bricks. In the red box, there are 2:3 purple to green bricks. In the white box, there are 5:2 brown to black bricks. If there are 80 bricks in each box, how many green bricks are there altogether? _____

End of test

Score:	Time taken:	Target met?

Use the information given to answer each sum. Write your answer as a **letter**.

Example A = 4   B = 2   C = 3   D = 6   E = 10   **A + D =** ___E___   (4 + 6 = 10)

1. A = 7   B = 12   C = 2   D = 6   E = 36   **(E × C) ÷ D =** _____

2. A = 6   B = 56   C = 86   D = 180   E = 76   **(D ÷ A) + B =** _____

3. A = 210   B = 78   C = 40   D = 92   E = 200   **B + D + C =** _____

4. A = 4   B = 16   C = 80   D = 12   E = 24   **(E × A) – B =** _____

5. A = 400   B = 54   C = 5   D = 26   E = 16   **(A ÷ C) – B =** _____

In each group, three words go together and two are the odd ones out. Underline the **two** words that do **not** go with the other three.

Example comprehend   understand   <u>confuse</u>   <u>unsure</u>   grasp

6. bridge   arc   ship   ark   yacht

7. sensible   mute   dumb   silly   speechless

8. treasure   prise   cherish   prize   lever

9. fake   reel   genuine   real   authentic

0. sorrow   melody   sadness   melancholy   jealousy

Using the alphabet to help you, find the letter pair that completes each sentence. Write it on the line.

A B C D E F G H I J K L M N O P Q R S T U V W X Y Z

Example **XY** is to **TU** as **NO** is to ___JK___.   (–4, –4)

1. **HS** is to **SH** as **PK** is to _____.

2. **WV** is to **SD** as **NC** is to _____.

13. **MN** is to **TG** as **BA** is to _____.

14. **PD** is to **KW** as **FY** is to _____.

Work out the answers. Write your answers on the lines.

5. Razia has four coins. Together the coins add up to £1.25. She has two **10** pence coins. What are the other two coins that Razia has? _____ and _____

6. Jerry has a bag with three items in it. The bag weighs **3.75** kg. He takes out of the bag a pair of binoculars which weigh **2.5** kg. He puts into the bag a compass which weighs **0.8** kg. How much does the bag weigh now? _____

End of test.

Score:		Time taken:		Target met?	

Underline the two words, **one** from each group, that will complete the sentence i the best way.

> **Example Mother** is to (lady, home, <u>daughter</u>) as **father** is to (<u>son</u>, old, beard).

1. **Microscope** is to (magnify, bacteria, slide) as **microphone** is to (singer, amplify, signify).
2. **Reckless** is to (careful, careless, colourful) as **arrogant** is to (superior, trusting, restful).
3. **Tournament** is to (win, joust, contest) as **bird** is to (roost, fowl, nest).
4. **Snips** is to (spun, spoon, spins) as **loots** is to (stool, lots, tools).
5. **Order** is to (chaos, demand, regulate) as **peculiar** is to (miniature, truth, usual).

Find the missing number in each sequence. Write it on the line.

> **Example** 20 22 24 26 28 <u> 30 </u> (+2 each time)

6. 1 4 9 16 _____ 36
7. –18 _____ –6 0 6 12
8. _____ 0 –4 –2 –6 –4

9. 240 120 60 30 15 _____
10. 90 65 50 _____ 10 –15

Find **one** missing letter that completes **both** pairs of words. Write it on the line.

> **Example** truc [<u>k</u>] ite   lic [<u>k</u>] now

11. tou [__] ude   blu [__] asp
12. ja [__] ell   pa [__] aste

13. grap [__] arm   fait [__] ush
14. cor [__] udge   daw [__] ovel

Work out the answers. Write your answers on the lines.

15. Stan sorts out his ties. He has **18** stripey, **12** spotty and **6** plain ties. One-third of the spotty ties are white and red, one-third are blue and green and the rest are black and silver. Half the stripey ties are striped in green and black, the rest are striped in white and red. Half the plain ties are red and the rest are grey. How many ties have red on them? _____

16. Six people are waiting at a bus stop. Marjory is wearing a hat, gloves, boots and a scarf. Ahmed is wearing a scarf and gloves but no hat. Tina is wearing gloves, a scarf and boots. Melvin is wearing boots, a hat, a scarf but no gloves. Leonard is wearing trainers and a hat. Morag is wearing boots, a scarf, hat and gloves. How many gloves are there altogether? _____

End of tes

Score: _____ Time taken: _____ Target met? _____

Target time: **10 minutes**

Find the missing number in each equation. Write it on the line.

Example $4 + 3 = 2 + \underline{\quad 5 \quad}$

1. $(250 \div 10) \times 2 = 5000 \div \underline{\quad\quad}$
2. $(140 - 50) \div 2 = 45 + \underline{\quad\quad}$
3. $7^2 + 8^2 = 200 - \underline{\quad\quad}$
4. $3(40 + 20) = 2 \times \underline{\quad\quad}$
5. $111 - 99 = 4^2 - \underline{\quad\quad}$

Underline the pair of words that are most **opposite** in meaning.

Example (<u>under, over</u>) (aloof, aloft) (irritate, anger)

6. (magnetic, metallic) (attract, repel) (force, drift)
7. (survive, suffer) (morbid, deathly) (live, dead)
8. (flawless, blemished) (polished, glossy) (scuffed, stretched)
9. (marriage, separate) (harvest, reap) (fertile, barren)
0. (youthful, aged) (mature, wise) (decrepit, recent)

Match the number codes to the words. One code is missing. Use these to help you work out the answers to the questions. Write your answers on the lines.

FRAME   MORE   FARM   FREER   5198   59183   8793

What is the code for:

1. **ROAM**? _____   12. **FAME**? _____   13. **REAR**? _____
4. What does the code **75539** mean? _____

Circle the letter next to the **true** statement for each question.

5. Miss Chan teaches chemistry to secondary school students. Chemistry is a science.

If the above statements are true, which one of the following statements must also be true?
A. Miss Chan writes books about chemistry.   D. Scientists wear goggles.
B. Chemists like setting fire to things.   E. Chemistry experiments are dangerous.
C. Miss Chan is a science teacher.

6. Mandeep is an optician. Opticians test people's eyesight and prescribe special lenses.

If the above statements are true, which one of the following statements must also be true?
A. Spectacles have lenses in them.   D. Mandeep is short-sighted.
B. Mandeep is having her eyes tested.   E. Mandeep tests people's eyesight.
C. Opticians wear glasses.

End of test.

Score:		Time taken:		Target met?	

Schofield&Sims

the long-established educational publisher specialising in maths, English and science

Verbal Reasoning 5 is a collection of short, language-based problem solving tests. Each timed test includes age-appropriate questions, providing opportunities for children to practise and master verbal reasoning skills in preparation for the 11+ and other school selection tests. This book is part of the **Rapid Reasoning Tests** series and covers the following question types: word and letter patterns; vocabulary; spelling; number patterns and problem solving.

Rapid Reasoning Tests provides short, effective, timed tests in reasoning. The series comprises six books of verbal reasoning tests and six books of non-verbal reasoning tests.

Written by experienced teachers and designed for independent use, **Rapid Reasoning Tests** has been carefully structured to provide practice of key, standard format question types. Each collection of tests has been designed for use over one year and provides one section per term in order to support regular practice.

Key features

- **Short tests** requiring few resources that are easy to fit into a busy timetable.
- A **target time** for each test encourages children to work quickly and develop the necessary exam skills for success in the 11+ and other tests.
- **Pull-out answers** in the centre of each book can be easily removed.
- **Free downloads** to support the series are available from the Schofield & Sims website.

The full series includes the following books:

Verbal Reasoning 1 978 07217 1238 3	**Non-verbal Reasoning 1** 978 07217 1226 0	**(Ages 6–7)**
Verbal Reasoning 2 978 07217 1239 0	**Non-verbal Reasoning 2** 978 07217 1227 7	**(Ages 7–8)**
Verbal Reasoning 3 978 07217 1240 6	**Non-verbal Reasoning 3** 978 07217 1228 4	**(Ages 8–9)**
Verbal Reasoning 4 978 07217 1241 3	**Non-verbal Reasoning 4** 978 07217 1229 1	**(Ages 9–10)**
Verbal Reasoning 5 978 07217 1242 0	**Non-verbal Reasoning 5** 978 07217 1230 7	**(Ages 10–11)**
Verbal Reasoning 6 978 07217 1243 7	**Non-verbal Reasoning 6** 978 07217 1231 4	**(Ages 11–12)**

MIX
Paper from responsible sources
FSC® C110589

ISBN 978-07217-1242-0

9 780721 712420

ISBN 978 07217 1242 0
Key Stage 2
Age range 10–11
£3.95
(Retail price)

For further information and to place an order visit
www.schofieldandsims.co.uk or telephone 01484 607080

Schofield&Sims

Verbal Reasoning 5

Rapid Reasoning Tests

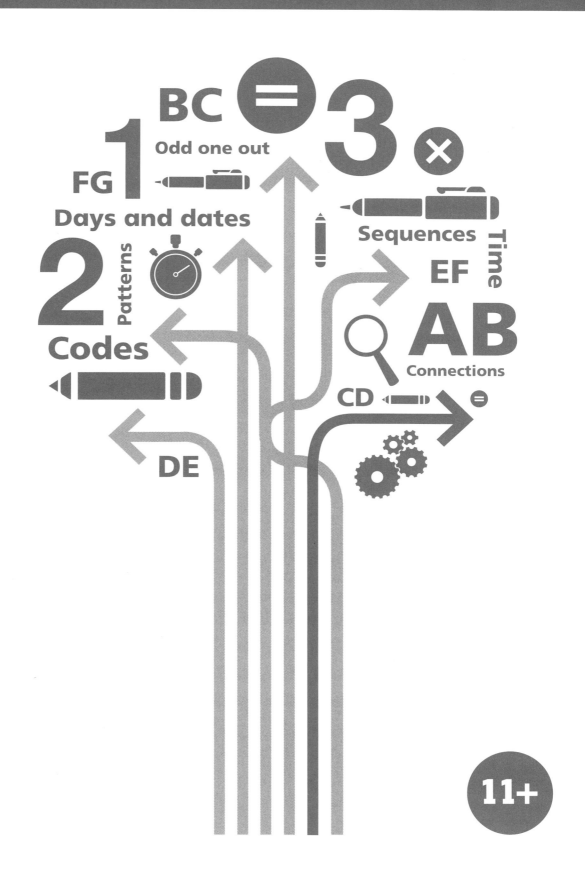

BC

Odd one out

FG **1**

Days and dates

2 Patterns

Codes

DE

3

Sequences

EF

Time

AB

Connections

CD

11+

Name

Introduction

The **Rapid Reasoning Tests** give you practice in answering verbal reasoning questions – all of them similar to those found in the 11+, 12+, 13+ and other school selection tests. As selection tests are usually timed, it is important that you learn to answer reasoning questions quickly as well as accurately. To check how quickly you are working, you should time how long you spend on every test in this book.

What you need

- A pencil
- An eraser
- A sheet of rough paper
- A clock, watch or stopwatch
- An adult to help you to mark the test (and to time how long you take – if you prefer not to do this yourself)

What to do

- Turn to **Section 1 Test 1** on page 4. Look at the purple box, labelled **Target time**. This tells you how long the test should take.

- When you are ready to start, check the time and write it down or start the stopwatch.

- Find the symbol ↓ near the top of the first page. This takes you to the instructions for the first set of questions. Read the instructions carefully.

- Look at the **Example** below the instructions. Decide why the answer given is correct. Work out the method used for finding it.

- Using similar methods, work carefully but quickly through each question. Do your best and try to answer every question. But, if you do get stuck on a question, leave it and go on to the next.

- When you reach the words **End of test**, write down the time shown on your clock or stop the stopwatch.

- Using the start and finish times that you have noted, work out how long you took to answer the questions. Then fill in the **Time taken** box.

- Ask an adult to mark your work for you using the pull-out answers section. Together complete the Score and **Target met?** boxes.

- Always have another go at questions that you got wrong without looking at the solutions.

- Later you will complete further tests. You will soon learn to find the correct answers more quickly. The adult who is helping you will tell you what to do next.

Published by Schofield & Sims Ltd,
Dogley Mill, Fenay Bridge, Huddersfield HD8 0NQ, UK
Telephone 01484 607080
www.schofieldandsims.co.uk

Copyright © Schofield & Sims Ltd, 2014

Author: **Siân Goodspeed**. Siân Goodspeed has asserted her moral right under the Copyright, Designs and Patents Act, 1988, to be identified as the author of this work.

British Library Cataloguing in Publication Data. A catalogue record for this book is available from the British Library.

Commissioned by **Carolyn Richardson Publishing Services** (www.publiserve.co.uk)

Design by **Oxford Designers & Illustrators**
Front cover design by **Ledgard Jepson Ltd**
Printed in India by **Multivista Global Ltd**

ISBN 978 07217 1242 0